PLAY *it* RIGHT
GUITAR ANTHEMS
LEARN 8 GREAT SONGS ON GUITAR
DAVID HARRISON

Published by
Wise Publications
14-15 Berners Street,
London W1T 3LJ, UK.

Exclusive Distributors:
Music Sales Limited
Distribution Centre, Newmarket Road,
Bury St Edmunds, Suffolk IP33 3YB, UK.
Music Sales Corporation
180 Madison Avenue, 24th Floor,
New York NY 10016, USA.
Music Sales Pty Limited
Units 3-4, 17 Willfox Street, Condell Park
NSW 2200, Australia.

Order No. AM1005356
ISBN 978-1-78038-712-3

Edited by Toby Knowles.
Music processing and layout by shedwork.com

Printed in the EU.

PLAY *it* RIGHT
GUITAR ANTHEMS
LEARN 8 GREAT SONGS ON GUITAR
DAVID HARRISON

Wise Publications
part of The Music Sales Group
London/New York/Paris/Sydney/Copenhagen/Berlin/Madrid/Hong Kong/Tokyo

Contents

Introduction

Here are a few pointers to get the best from this book... and the DVD too.

Using the DVD

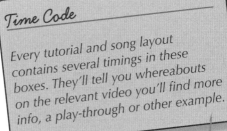

Time Code

Every tutorial and song layout contains several timings in these boxes. They'll tell you whereabouts on the relevant video you'll find more info, a play-through or other example.

On the DVD, you'll find a full tutorial video for every song that's in the book. Each video looks at the most important features of the song, including all the chord shapes and some essential techniques—

Watch out for the time code symbols in the book (*left*). Whenever you see this, you'll know what section of the video to watch for more info or to hear an example. The time shown is the time of the particular track on the DVD.

such as strumming or picking patterns— before playing each section of the song through. Finally there's a run-though of the entire song using professionally produced backing tracks.

Reading Repeats

Repeat Marks

Music between these two symbols is repeated. Go back to the first symbol and play again from there.

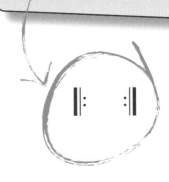

In written music, repeated sections are often used to show a section that's played more than once. Repeats might be immediate (verse 2 following directly on

The simplest kind of repeat is one between the two repeat marks (*left*). These *repeat marks* embrace a passage to be repeated.

from verse 1, for example) or they might be a return to a passage from earlier on in the song. There are specific ways to show both kinds of repeats.

Simply play the section through and, when you finish it, play it again from the start of the section.

Repeat Endings

The square brackets above the music show different endings for the first and second time through a repeated section: the endings are numbered.

Repeated sections like this often have different endings on the first and second play through. These are shown by square

brackets over the endings, known as *first* and *second time* bars. Sometimes you'll even see third or fourth time bars.

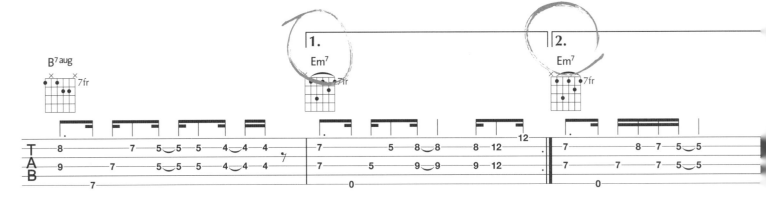

More Repeats: Segno and Coda

Another common type of repeat occurs when the music returns to a section played earlier in the song. This is often followed by a jump to the ending.

Look out for this symbol 𝄋, called a *segno*. This shows where to return to. You'll be sent there by an instruction at the end of a section: *D. S.* which stands for *dal segno* ('from the sign').

Generally, when you're playing from the 𝄋 you're headed towards the *coda*, the final section of the song. So watch out for the ⊕ symbol. You'll see *To coda*, which is telling you to jump to the *Coda* section.

D.S.

Dal Segno

Watch out for a D.S. at the end of a section. It sends you back to the 𝄋 symbol. This often leads to a coda.

Coda

The coda (meaning 'tail' in Italian) is the last section of a song. It's signalled with ⊕. It might include a final chorus or outro. Look for the 'To coda' instruction.

Where you're sent to the 𝄋 first, you'll see 'D.S. al Coda' meaning 'from the sign, to the coda'.

Chord Boxes

The vertical lines represent the guitar strings from the bottom string (left) to the top string (right).

The horizontal lines are the fret wires, and the nut is shown as a thick line at the top.

Open strings are shown with 'o', strings not played with 'x'.

Fret numbers are shown when the nut is out of view.

Which Way Up?

These diagrams are drawn as if the guitar was standing upright.

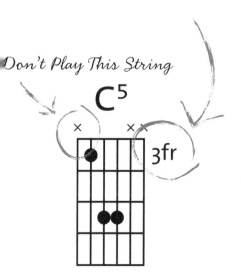

Don't Play This String

C⁵

3fr

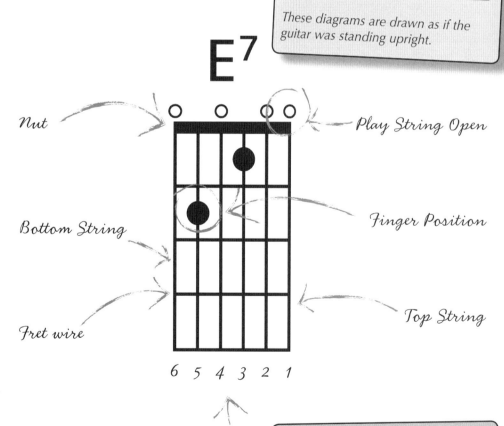

E⁷

Nut

Bottom String

Fret wire

Play String Open

Finger Position

Top String

6 5 4 3 2 1

String Numbers

Strings are numbered from top (1st) to bottom (6th).

Highway To Hell

This 1979 classic is the title track from AC/DC's sixth studio album, which was the last to feature singer Bon Scott. With just two riffs and a handful of chords, this rocker has become a firm favourite with guitarists.

00:44

Intro and Verse Riff

The famous riff that opens the song continues as the basis for the verse, too. It uses just three chords strummed in an eighth-note rhythm.

It's pretty easy to play, but you'll need to count carefully and pay special attention to the precise rhythmic placement of each strum.

Reading the Dots

In the song, the riff is written in full tab, but the rhythm coupled with the chord shapes used gives you all the info you really need to play this part.

Using a standard down-up strumming, certain parts of the riff are naturally played with an up-strum and others strummed down. For instance, the riff begins halfway

through the third beat, with three eighth-notes played in succession, meaning it's played up-down-up. Here's the whole of the riff with strum directions indicated:

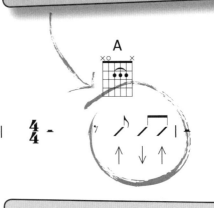

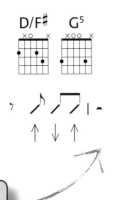

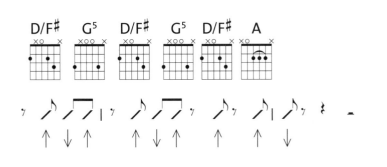

Playing Rests

Be sure to create silence in between the strummed sections by bringing the strumming hand down onto the strings, momentarily muting them.

Fretting the Chord Shapes

The bottom note of the D/F♯ shape can be fretted with the thumb if you prefer. Alternatively use the first finger.

To mute the 5th string, lightly touch the string with whichever finger you use to fret the 6th string. Angus Young uses his thumb, but you might the first finger more comfortable.

Likewise, the top string is muted with the finger that frets the 2nd string.

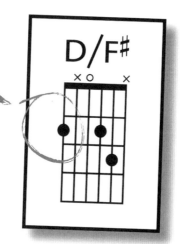

Chorus

In the chorus, the chord shapes are allowed to ring on rather than being cut short with muting. The A shape is now reduced to a simple three-string version, making a power chord of A⁵.

This is played for a whole bar, giving way on the very last half-beat to a D chord. Play the D with an accented up-strum, letting the sound continue until the following up-strum.

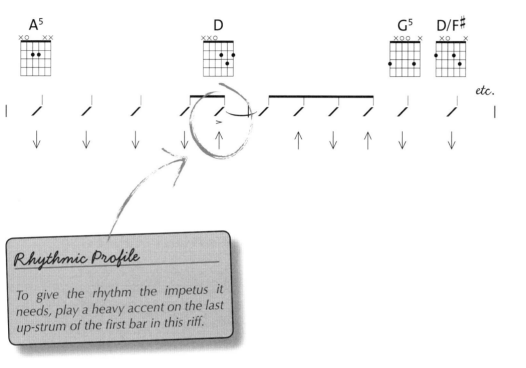

Rhythmic Profile

To give the rhythm the impetus it needs, play a heavy accent on the last up-strum of the first bar in this riff.

Chorus 2 Ending

At the end of the second chorus, just before the guitar solo, there's a short four-bar section with two new chord shapes: Dsus⁴/A and D/A.

As before, timing is key here. Take it slowly at first, being sure to pay attention to the strumming direction. Here's the section in full:

Chord Changes

Alternating between these two shapes is just a question of moving the little finger on and off the 3rd fret of the top string.

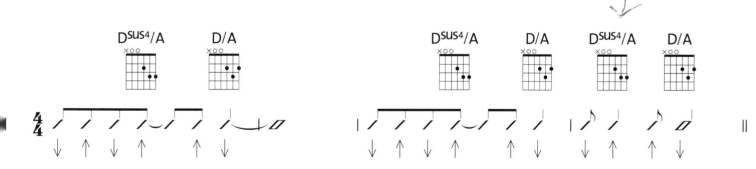

Highway To Hell

Words & Music by Angus Young, Malcolm Young & Bon Scott

Where The Streets Have No Name

The opening track from U2's 1987 album The Joshua Tree, *produced by Daniel Lanois and Brian Eno, is concerned with religious segregation in Belfast. It's a long song, but the repeating guitar parts are straightforward.*

Guitar Sound

`00:18`

The Edge's trademark guitar sound is acheived through a combination of compression—reducing the difference in volume between the quieter and louder sounds, creating an overall fuller sound; chorus—which thickens the sound by adding a slightly detuned 'copy' onto the original; and delay.

Delay Settings

Set the delay for an interval of around 200 milliseconds. The 'echo' should occur halfway between the eighth-notes, creating a doubling sound—in effect making sixteenths.

Guitar → **Comp.** → **Chorus** → **Delay** → *Amp*

`02:00`

Playing the Intro

Although the harmony changes (and different chord shapes are given) the guitar continues to play the same figure throughout the intro.

After an eight-bar section on organ, the guitar enters with eighth-notes played on the top three strings, for a further 16 bars, like so:

Chord Shapes

Unless you're strumming through the chords, play the lead guitar line and ignore the chord shapes.

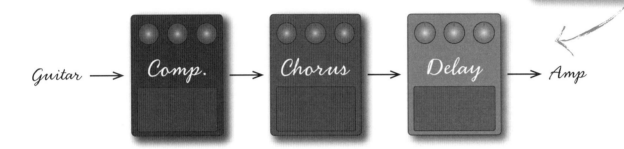

D⁵

etc.

Eventually, as the time signature changes to four-in-the-bar, the guitar strums in sixteenth-notes. This begins at the end of the final 3/4 bar (*right*):

Strumming Directions

Although arrows are often used to show the strumming direction in rhythms, in full guitar tab, symbols more commonly found in violin music are used: ⊓ shows a down-strum, while ∨ indicates an up-strum.

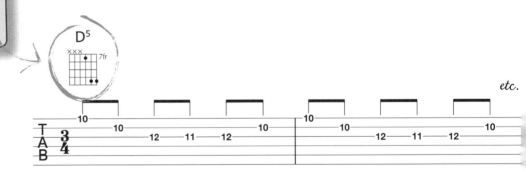

Now we continue in 4/4 until verse 1 begins. The initial syncopated figure might need some extra attention.

Have a look at the video example and take care with the strumming direction, and it'll fall into place soon enough.

In the second bar of this example, the four-note held chord shape has a moving note on the 3rd string.

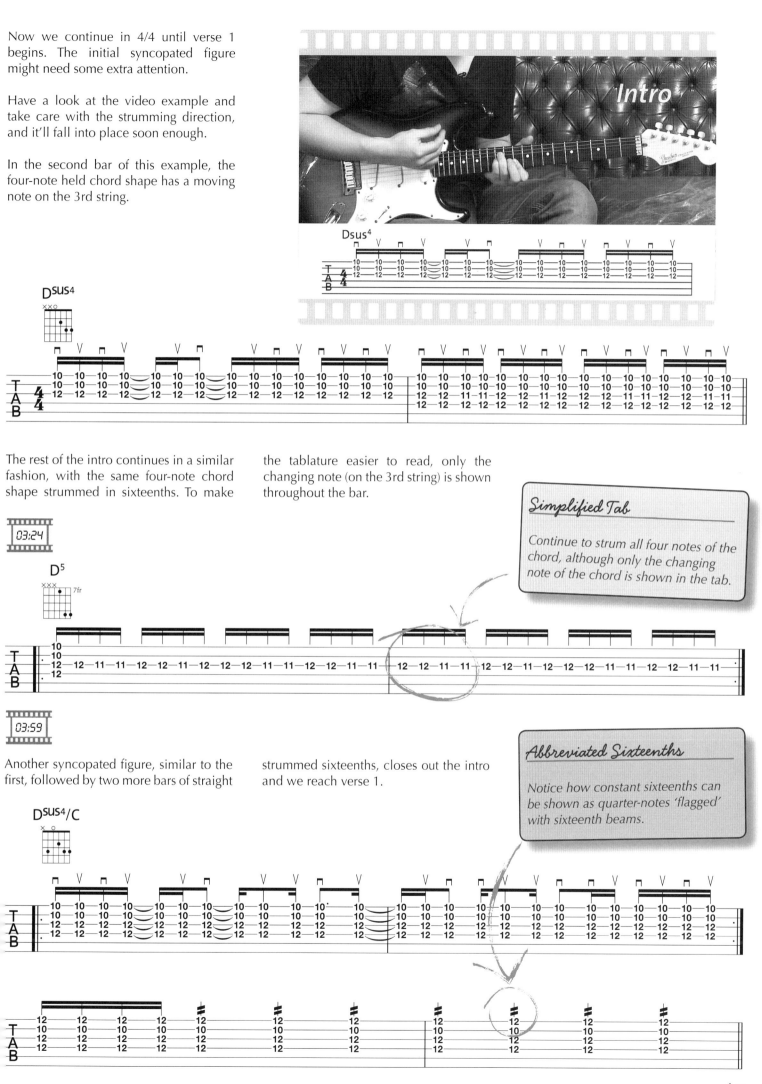

The rest of the intro continues in a similar fashion, with the same four-note chord shape strummed in sixteenths. To make the tablature easier to read, only the changing note (on the 3rd string) is shown throughout the bar.

Simplified Tab

Continue to strum all four notes of the chord, although only the changing note of the chord is shown in the tab.

Another syncopated figure, similar to the first, followed by two more bars of straight strummed sixteenths, closes out the intro and we reach verse 1.

Abbreviated Sixteenths

Notice how constant sixteenths can be shown as quarter-notes 'flagged' with sixteenth beams.

Creating the Right Sound

For the authentic guitar part, disregard the chord shapes shown, aiming instead for a rhythmic effect.

Verse 1

The sixteenth-note strumming continues into the verse, but now with an indistinct, percussive sound.

Rest the fretting hand lightly on the strings to dampen them and strum the rhythms shown.

Of course, if you want a fuller sound, you're free to strum the chords shown, too—preferably in sixteenths!

At the end of the verse, the four bars of Csus² are played 'properly', fretting the shape to make a recognisable chord (*left*).

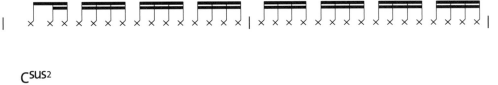

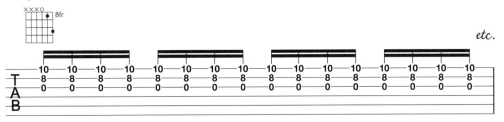

Verse 2

As the verse repeats, the original guitar part plays as before. Now a second guitar enters with held chords and some single-note picking too.

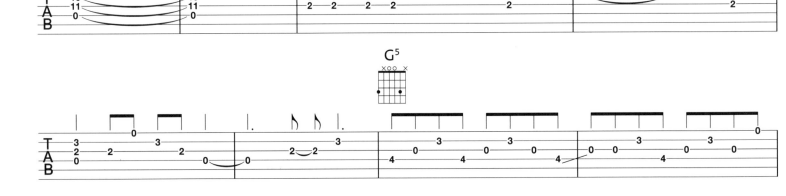

After eight bars, the second guitar strums in sixteenths for four bars on a single shape, like so:

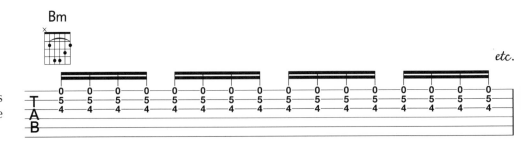

Finally, verse 2 closes out with four bars of the same Csus² strumming that ends verse 1, taking us into the chorus.

Chorus 1

In the chorus, either play the indicated shapes in sixteenths, or else play the tablature. To make it easier to read, the tab again uses the abbreviated notation:

Tab or Chords?

As in the verses, the original guitar part largely differs from the given chord shapes.

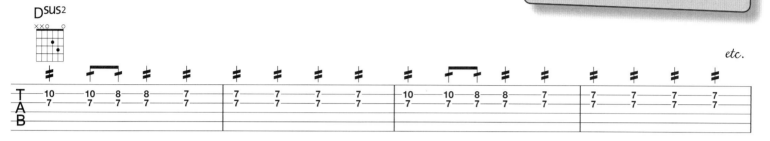

After 12 bars in a similar fashion, the chorus ends with another four bars of the strummed figure we first saw towards the end of the intro.

As before, the tab is simplified to show only the notes that change (*right*):

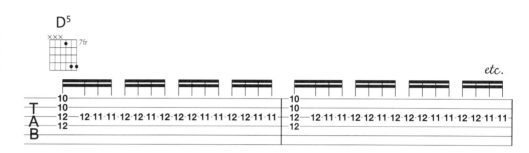

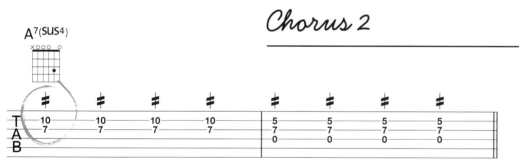

Chorus 2

Chorus 2 is identical to the first chorus until the 12th bar—now, a new variation is played on A^7sus^4, taking us into the coda, and eventually to the outro.

In the coda, the D^5 sixteenth figure is played over an extended chorus for a total of 20 bars until the outro is reached.

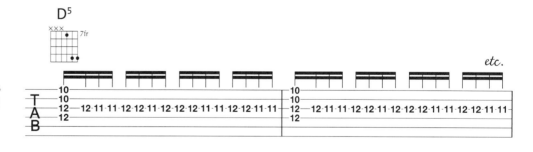

Outro

The outro sees a return to the original 3/4 figure that we saw in the intro. This repeats to a fade:

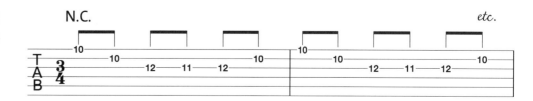

17

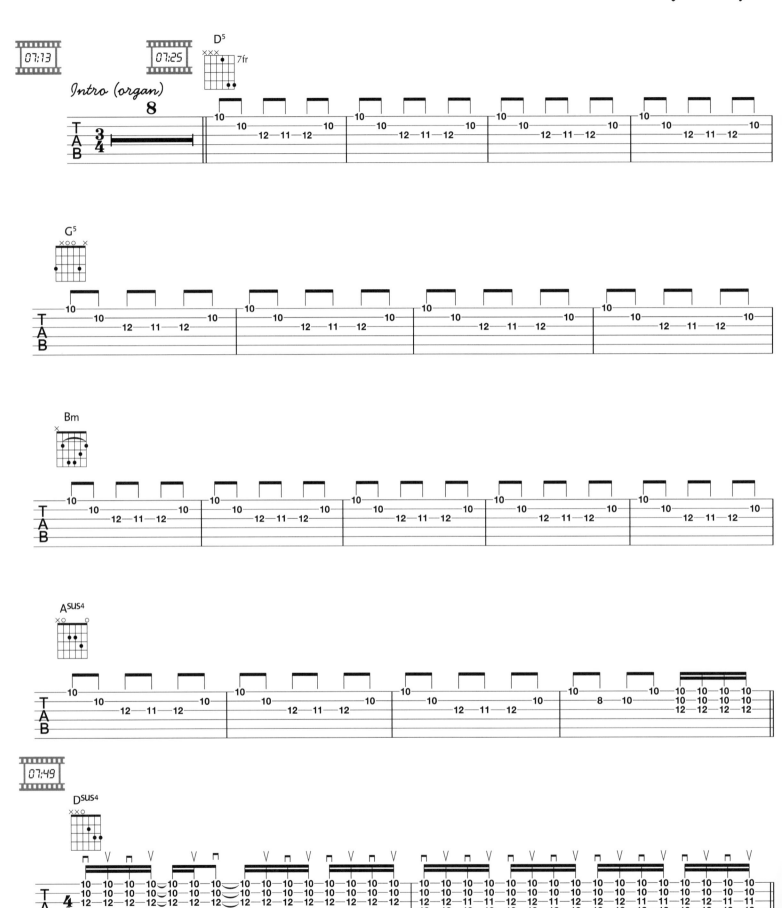

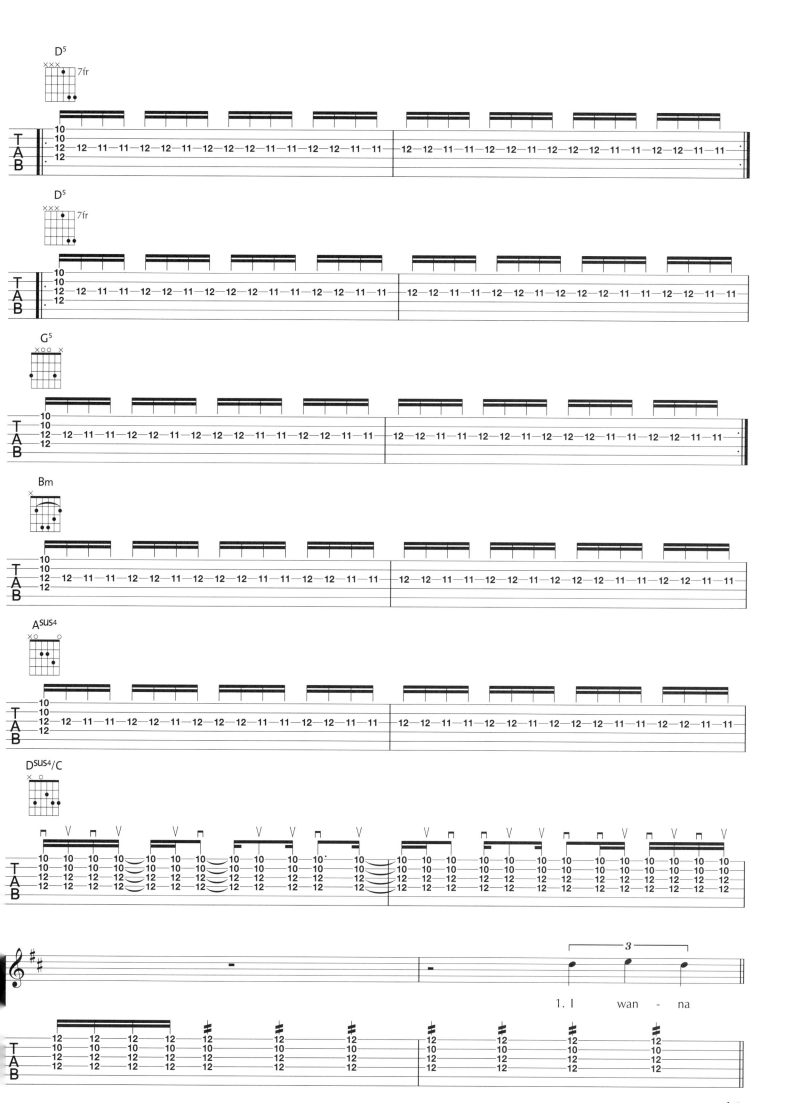

20

All Right Now

London blues-rock band Free released their signature tune in 1970. It's one of the most straightforward songs in the rock repertoire with just two main parts and some very simple chord shapes.

The Riff

Big Power Chord

This five-string A5 shape stretches over two octaves, making a powerful sound. You'll need to barre with your first finger on the 2nd fret, and with your fourth finger on the 5th fret.

The famous opening riff is a series of chord shapes beginning with an extended A^5 chord.

The D^5 chord that follows is best played by keeping the barre from the A^5 shape, adding notes to it on the 4th and 2nd strings—when you strum the shape, be sure not to play the top string.

To move on to the third chord, simply lift off the barre, replacing the notes fretted for the D^5 chord—this time letting the open top string sound.

Finally, the riff returns to the original A^5 shape, and the whole thing starts again. Memorise these four bars, since you'll be playing them a lot!

Naming the Chords

$D^{(add11)}/A$ *is a bit of a mouthful! On the video, the name is simplified to* A^7sus^4—*but it's the same chord...*

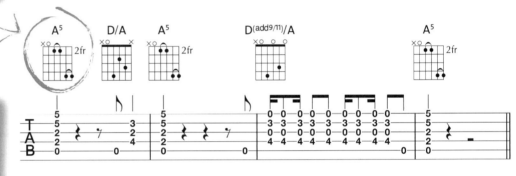

Once you've got the chord shapes 'under your fingers' it's time to tackle the rhythm. Apart from the third bar, strum everything with down-strokes to create a solid feel.

The eighth-notes on the open 5th string that anticipate the chords are quite subtle and can be *ghosted* (barely played) by just touching the string.

Here's how the strumming directions look for the whole phrase. In the third bar, strum as shown: it'll give you the room you need to manoeuvre.

The first and third beats contain groups of three strums—a sixteenth, an eighth and another sixteenth. Play the first sixteenth as a down-strum for emphasis, naturally leading to an up-strum.

Playing the final sixteenth as another up-strum means you'll be strumming down at the start of the next beat.

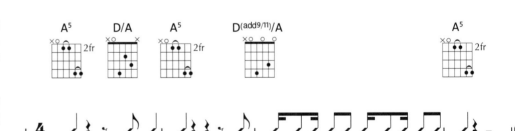

Strumming Direction

Take a moment to play the third bar slowly through a few times until it feels natural. Playing with confidence helps the music to flow freely.

Chorus

For the chorus, the guitar part employs a simple riff that uses just a couple of notes at a time.

Starting with a new A⁵ shape on the 7th fret, it drops two frets to G⁵ after a bar via two passing notes on the 5th string.

Notice that the G⁵ chord is anticipated (brought forward) by an eighth-note.

Now drop the 4th-string note by a fret for the D shape, before returning to the A⁵ chord in the final bar. Play this riff twice, and the chorus is complete!

> ### Fingers and Frets
>
> Throughout the chorus riff, keep the first finger on the lower note of each chord, using the third or fourth finger for the other notes—whichever you find easier.

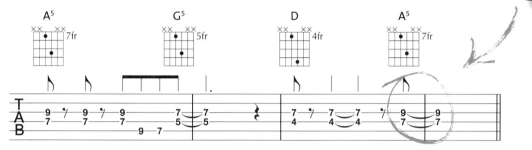

Guitar Solo Chords

A lengthy guitar solo follows the second chorus. Here, the backing guitar plays a repeated two-bar phrase a total of 17 times:

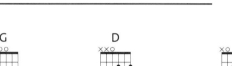

Eventually, a further bar of G and D leads to two bars of a chord of E. At this point the chorus kicks in once more and the song fades out.

Guitar Sound

Paul Kossoff's original heavy guitar sound is acheived with a Gibson Les Paul played very loudly through an overdriven Marshall amp, without any further effects.

To recreate the sound, apply overdrive, adding compression to emulate both the valve amp and the recording process. Now, add a touch of reverb to taste.

> ### Reverb Settings
>
> The reverb should be subtle. It's used here to create something like the acoustic sound of the original studio rather than an expansive, huge effect. You might decide to do without.

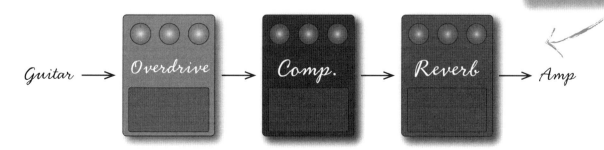

Drive My Car

This simple blues-inspired track that opens The Beatles' Rubber Soul has some catchy guitar parts that aren't too tricky to play. This song is great for two guitars, with one strumming the chords while the other plays the riffs.

Intro

`01:33`

The single-note Chuck Berry-style line that kicks off the song has a slide and a small bend, and ends with a pair of notes held over to the final bar.

This guitar part is played solo, before the rest of the band enters. It doesn't fit neatly into 4/4, so a 9/8 bar is inserted to represent the extra half-beat.

Fingers and Frets

Play the pairs of notes together with a single finger.

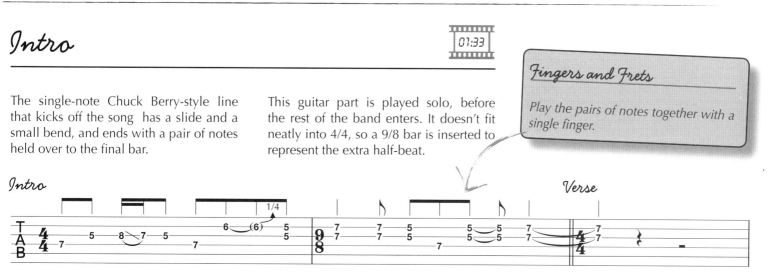

Verse

`03:09`

The strumming style for this song is a funky sixteenth-note feel. It's important to keep moving down-up-down-up even if you're not always making contact with the strings.

Here's an example with accents on beats 2 and 4—the 'backbeats' (*right*):

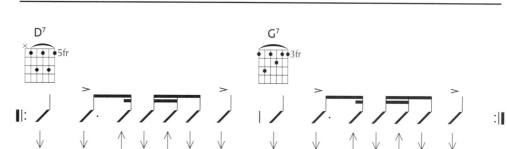

The riff (*below*) closely follows the bass guitar. Once you've played the first bar, on D⁷, the riff is displaced down a string

and two frets for the G⁷ bar. After three times through, there are two final bars on A⁷(♯9) ending on another similar phrase.

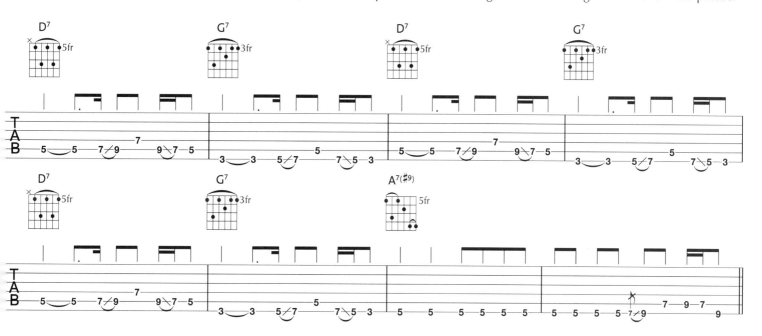

`05:34`

Careful Fingering

Take a good look at the video examples to see the precise fingering for these riffs.

Continue strumming over the chords indicated, or else play the single-note line in the chorus. It's almost exclusively played on the bottom string, initially alternating between B and G for five bars.

The line ends with two bars that change chords every two beats before a final bar that is identical to the closing bar of the verse. Try bars 6 and 7 slowly until they 'sit' under the fingers.

Chorus

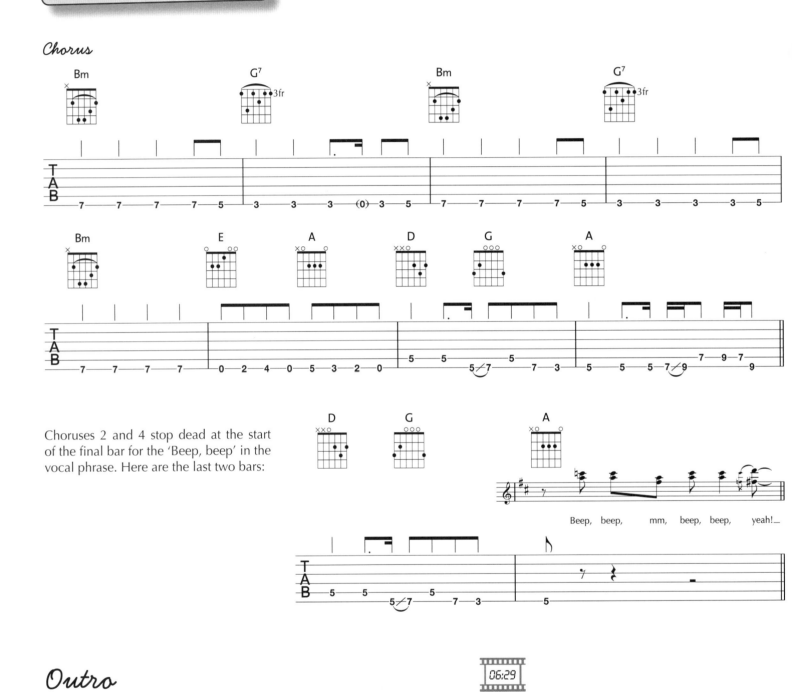

Choruses 2 and 4 stop dead at the start of the final bar for the 'Beep, beep' in the vocal phrase. Here are the last two bars:

Beep, beep, mm, beep, beep, yeah!__

Outro

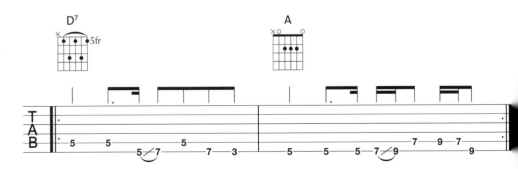
`06:29`

After two verses and choruses, a guitar solo—based on the verse structure—and a further two verses and choruses, we enter the outro.

Here, the final two bars of the chorus riff repeat to fade (*right*):

Drive My Car

Words & Music by John Lennon & Paul McCartney

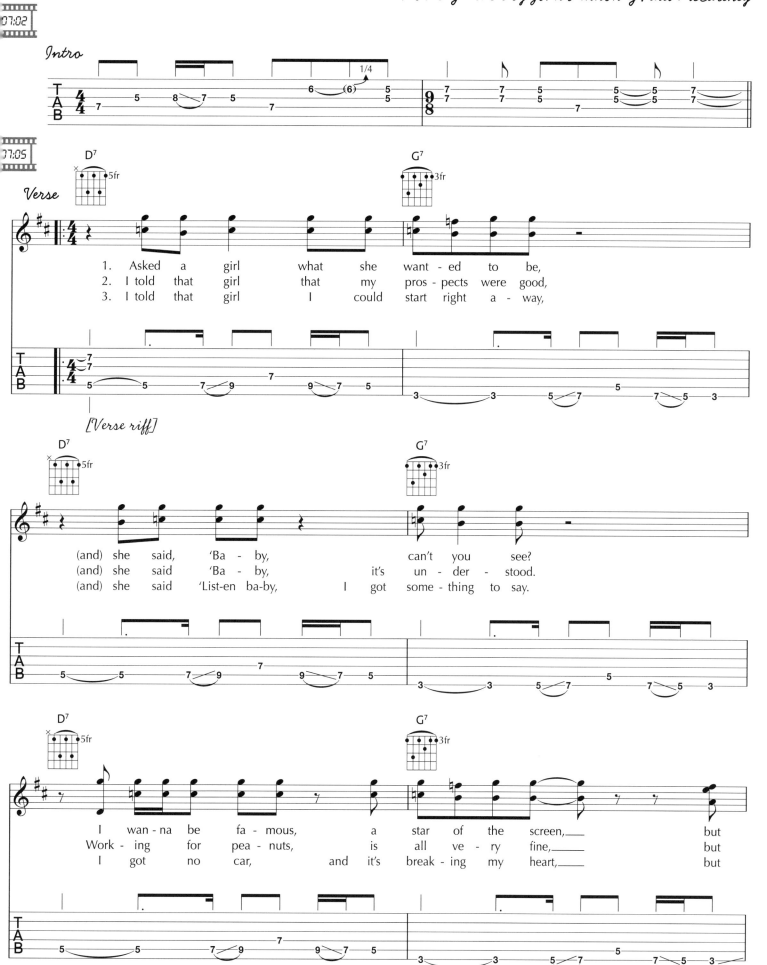

you can do some-thing   in be-tween.___
I can show you a   bet-ter time.___
I found a dri-ver and that's a   start.___

Chorus

Ba-by you can drive my car.___   Yes, I'm gon-na be a star.___

Ba-by you can drive my car,___   and may-be I love___

1.
___ you.'

2.   *To Coda*

Beep, beep, mm, beep, beep,   yeah!___

Guitar Solo

[Play verse riff]

[Lead guitar]

with slide

with slide

with slide

D.S. al Coda
with repeats

with slide

Coda

Repeat to fade

Beep, beep, mm, beep, beep, yeah!

Cigarettes & Alcohol

From Oasis' 1994 album Definitely Maybe, *this track is a glimpse at the band's wilder side. The influence of T. Rex and Chuck Berry can clearly be heard in the various guitar parts.*

Intro Riff

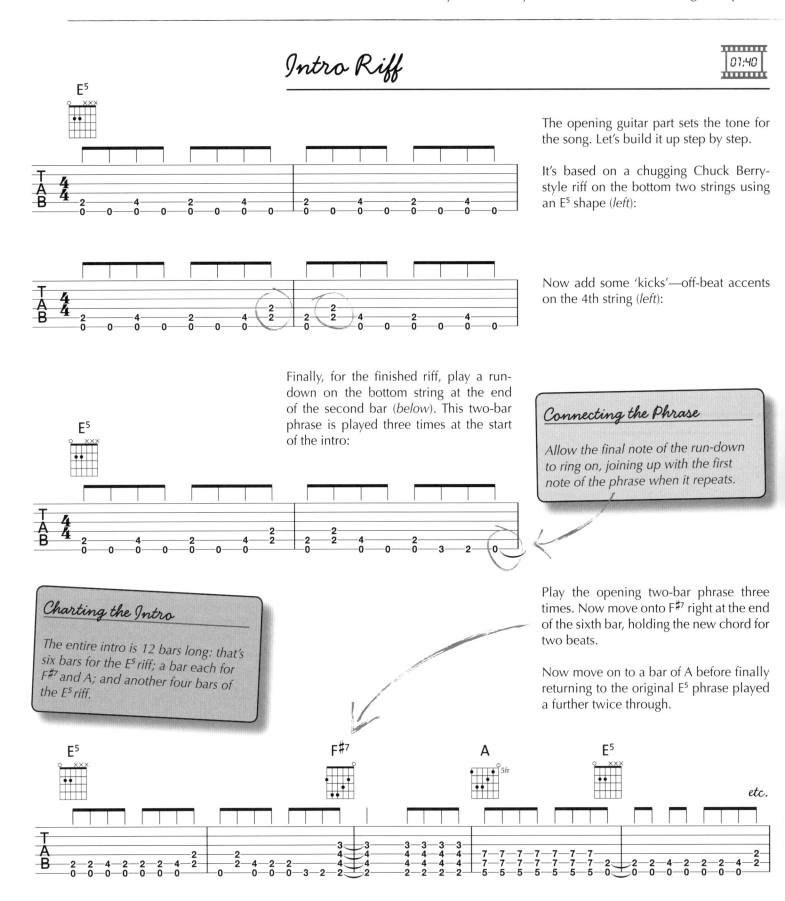

The opening guitar part sets the tone for the song. Let's build it up step by step.

It's based on a chugging Chuck Berry-style riff on the bottom two strings using an E⁵ shape (*left*):

Now add some 'kicks'—off-beat accents on the 4th string (*left*):

Finally, for the finished riff, play a run-down on the bottom string at the end of the second bar (*below*). This two-bar phrase is played three times at the start of the intro:

Connecting the Phrase

Allow the final note of the run-down to ring on, joining up with the first note of the phrase when it repeats.

Charting the Intro

The entire intro is 12 bars long: that's six bars for the E⁵ riff; a bar each for F♯7 and A; and another four bars of the E⁵ riff.

Play the opening two-bar phrase three times. Now move onto F♯7 right at the end of the sixth bar, holding the new chord for two beats.

Now move on to a bar of A before finally returning to the original E⁵ phrase played a further twice through.

etc.

34

Verse

Here are the first eight bars written out in rhythm slashes, which is how they're shown in the song (page 38). However, as indicated, you'll play the riff as shown in the intro tablature.

Musical Shorthand

The good news is, that once you've mastered the intro you can easily play the verse, too. The verse is played in exactly the same way, but this time there are just two bars of E^5 before moving on to $F^{\#7}$ and A, returning for another four bars of E^5. This makes eight bars altogether, which then repeat to make a verse.

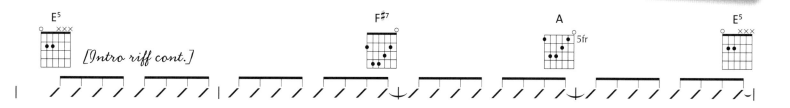

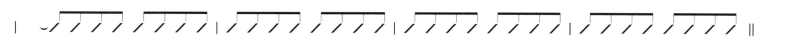

Repeated Sections

Play these eight bars twice through for a complete verse.

Pre-Chorus

The eight-bar section that comes between the verse and the chorus is made of alternating bars of A^5 and E^5, with a chord of $Dsus^2$ in the seventh bar.

The A^5 and E^5 chords are anticipated—that is, played an eighth-note before the start of the bar, much like the intro and verse.

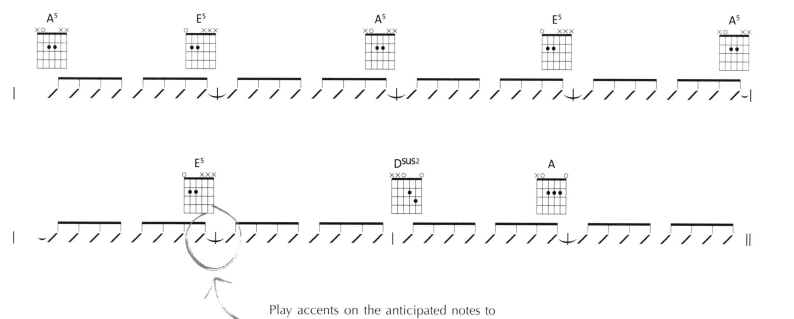

Play accents on the anticipated notes to emphasise the rhythm.

The chorus is a series of two-bar phrases played a total of four times, making eight bars in all.

Again, there are anticipated chords that can be accented:

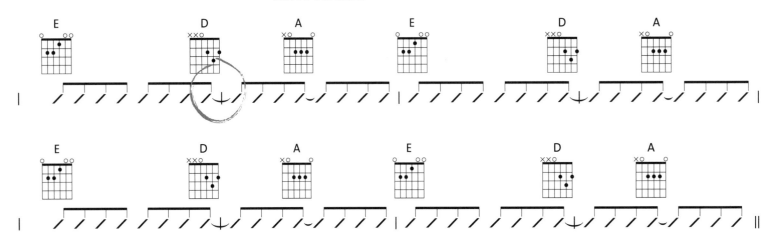

Instrumental

The first chorus is followed a two-bar single-note phrase (*below*). This heralds another 12-bar section that's an exact repeat of the intro.

Play a half-step bend & release on the 11th fret of the 3rd string, eventually moving down to the 9th fret. This is then repeated, starting on the 6th fret.

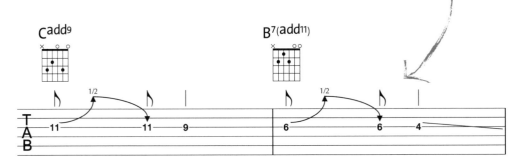

Outro

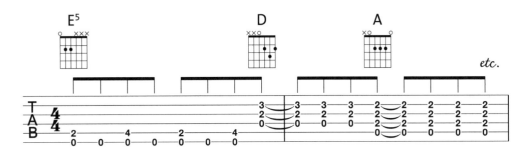

The second chorus is extended into an outro section in which the two-bar phrase chorus phrase is played another 16 times through.

You can combine this strummed phrase with a variation on the original intro riff like so (*left*):

The song eventually finishes on a single, held chord of E.

40

Layla

The twin electric guitars of Eric Clapton and Duane Allman make this 1971 release a true icon of rock history. The 2004 'unplugged' acoustic version brought this song fame with a new generation of listeners.

Playing the Intro Riff

The famous opening riff is easy enough to play, but needs a little bit of attention. It begins with a hammer-on from the open 5th string, which is followed by another—and a pull-off—on the open 4th string:

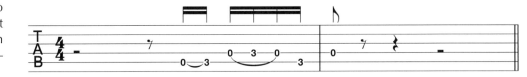

The first phrase is then linked to a series of power chords. D⁵ slides down to C⁵, and a couple of bass notes on the 6th string are required, too:

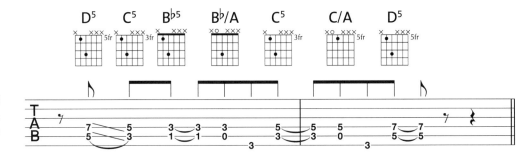

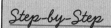

Step-by-Step

There are note-for-note explanations of these phrases in the video. Check them out for fingerings and timing.

When you're happy with these two phrases, it's time to put them together. Gradually increase the tempo until it comes naturally:

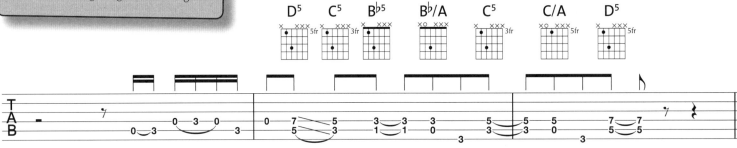

Bending Pitch

Take care over the tuning of your bends. Here it needs to be exactly a tone. If necessary, play the (unbent) note two frets higher for reference.

After four bars, the opening phrase is repeated two octaves higher, with a new second phrase featuring a full tone bend on the 13th fret:

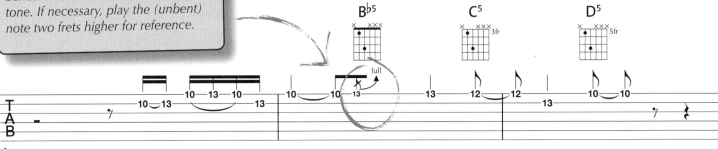

This whole phrase is repeated, but this time the bend is on the 15th fret.

Here's how these high phrases look when played together. Notice that on the repeat, the final note is changed and the section ends on a 2/4 bar.

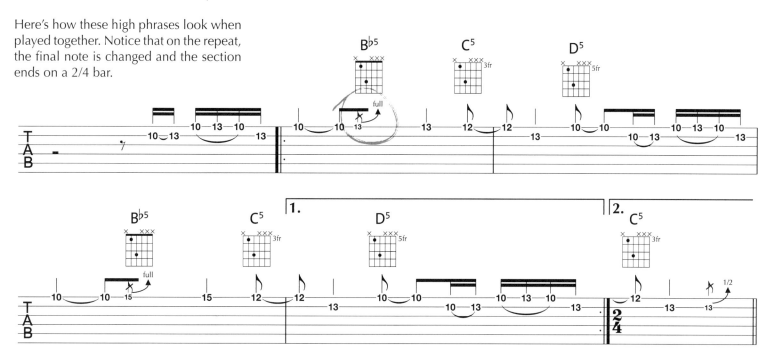

Meanwhile, throughout the intro section, a second guitar part plays an octave below the first guitar part (*right*):

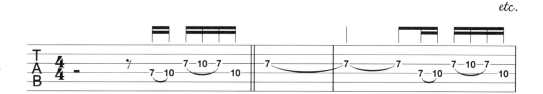

Verse

04:09

The chords in the verse are straightforward. They're strummed in straight quarter-notes, building to include some eighth- note and sixteenth-note strumming as the verse progresses. Here's a suggestion of the way this might be played:

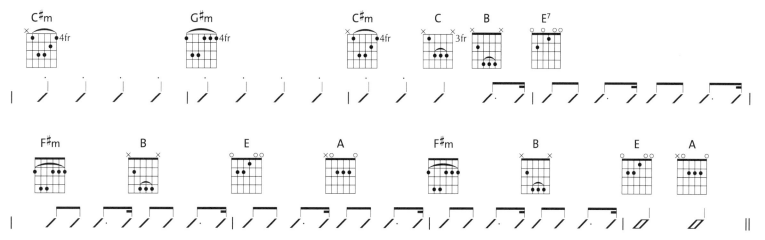

The outro opens up into a piano-based section. Eventually, the guitar re-enters with this classic Duane Allman phrase:

Now we have a series of arpeggios. The first eight bars are played twice, before another eight bar section:

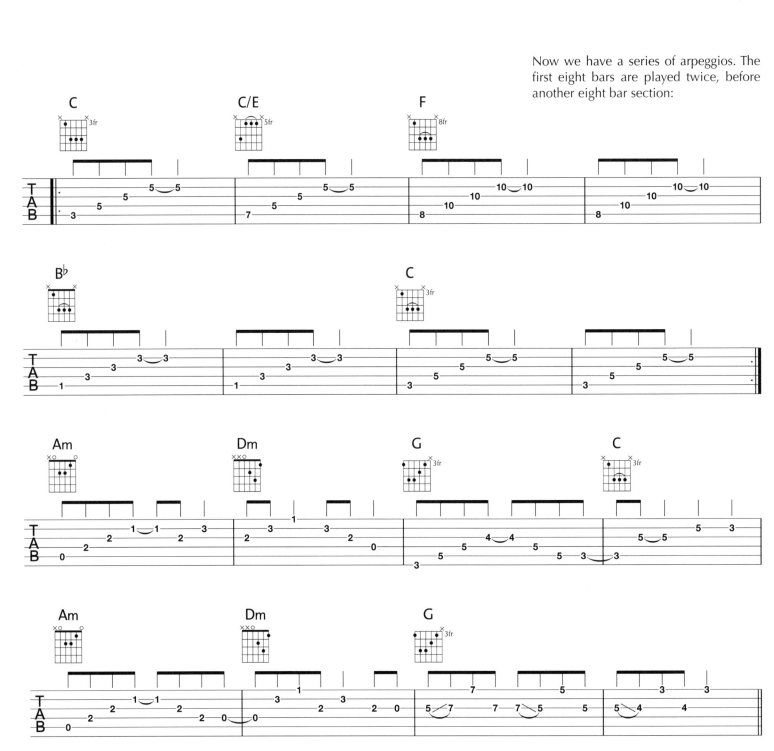

The various sections shown here are repeated—in different orders—for a total of almost four minutes.

The song ends on two final bars of B♭, slowing down to a single strummed chord of C.

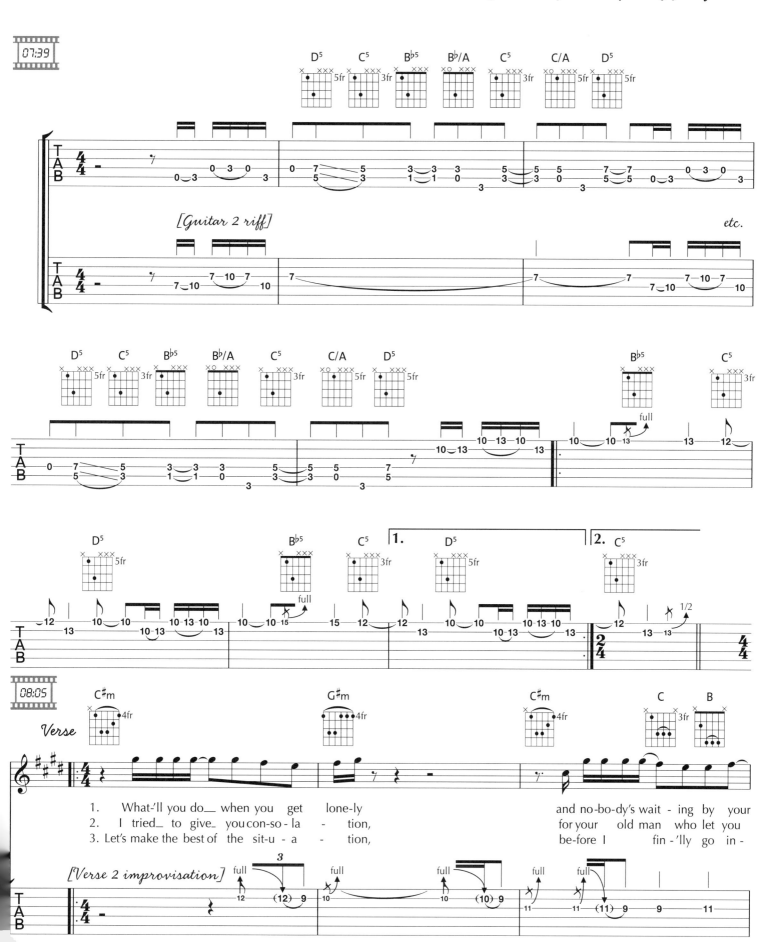

Verse

1.   What-'ll you do__ when you get   lone-ly   and no-bo-dy's wait - ing by your
2.   I tried__ to give__ you con-so-la   - tion,   for your   old man   who let you
3. Let's make the best of the sit-u-a   - tion,   be-fore I   fin -'lly go in-

[Verse 2 improvisation]

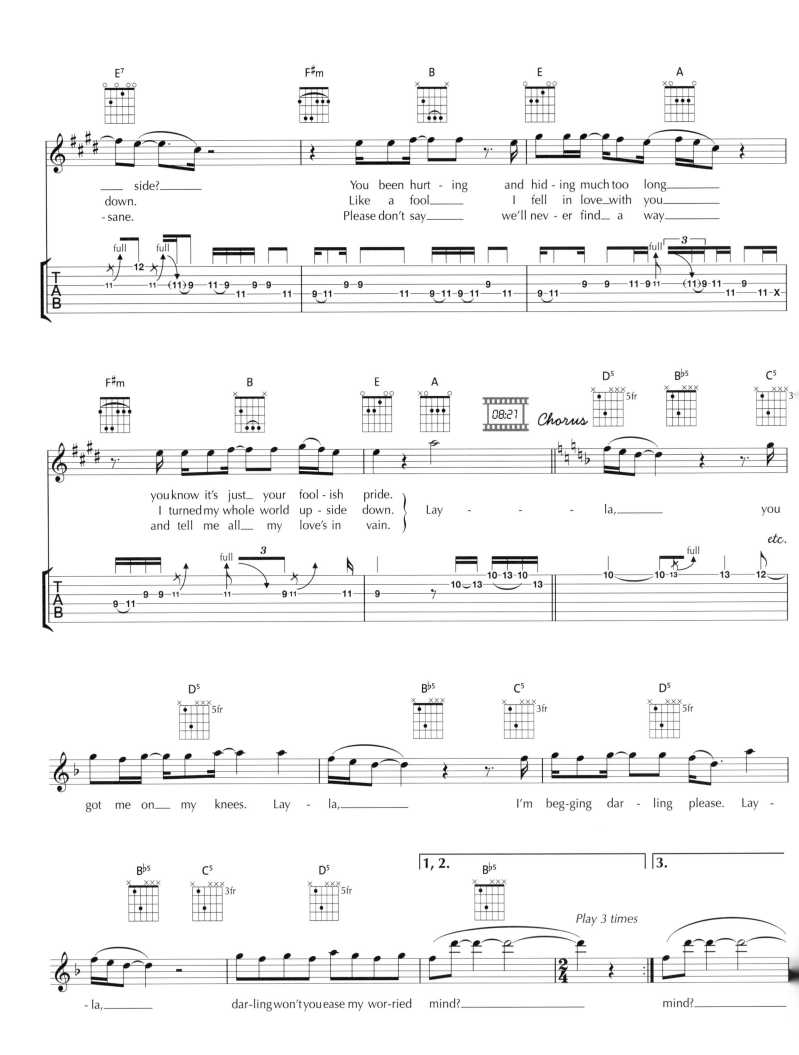

Lay - la,_____ you got me on__ my knees. Lay - la,_____ I'm

beg-ging dar - ling please. Lay - la,_____ dar - ling won't you ease my wor - ried

mind?_____ Lay - -

Piano
instrumental

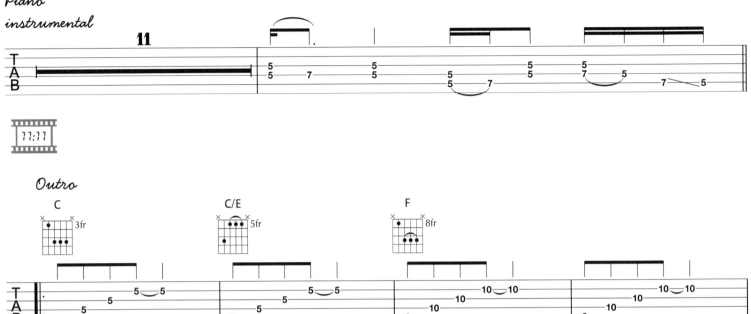

Outro

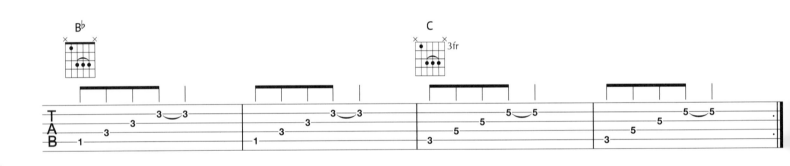

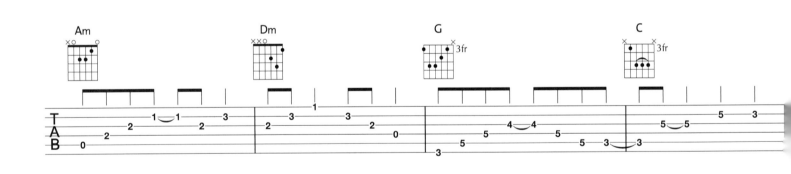

Repeat ad lib. to end

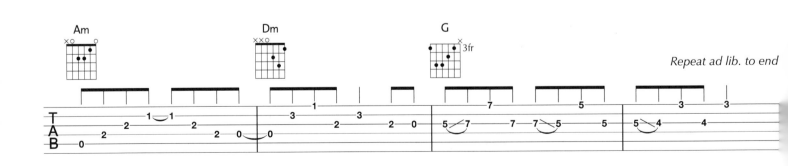

Message In A Bottle

From the 1979 Reggatta de Blanc *album, this track was the Police's first UK No. 1. As with many songs by the trio, the guitar part is extremely precise and might need a bit of practice—but it's very playable.*

The Riff

`07:24`

The instantly recognisable riff that opens the song is based on four very specific chord shapes.

Once you've got these shapes under your fingers, you'll be able to play the riff easily.

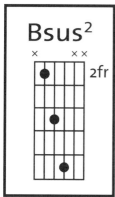
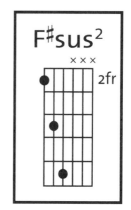

C#sus² (4fr)   Asus²   Bsus² (2fr)   F#sus² (2fr)

Visualising the Shapes

Notice how the chord shapes for the main riff resemble each other. The three fretted positions form a diagonal line on consecutive strings.

You might find these chord shapes a bit of a stretch to start with.

Be sure to keep your thumb well behind the neck to maximise the reach of your fingers onto the fretboard—especially for the fourth finger on the final note of each chord.

C#sus2   Asus2   Bsus2   F#sus2

```
T 4
A 4   8          4        6         6   7
B 4 6        2        4        4        
  4      0   0       2   2            2   2    4
```

Verse riff — Asus²

Sliding Up

The final pair of notes in the phrase is played by fretting on the 6th fret of the 4th string and sliding up to the 7th fret without picking the string again.

It's worth persevering with this riff, since it forms not only the intro, but also the verse—and the outro too!

Check out the video for alternative positions for some of these chords, but above all try to memorise the sequence so you can concentrate on playing rather than reading.

Tied Notes

The E⁵ chord is played half a beat early, but is then left to ring on into the next beat.

⟦03:35⟧

The chorus is in two sections: firstly, a series of power chords strummed in even eighth-notes; and then a sequence of sustained barre chords.

For the power chord strumming, play every strum as a down-stroke. It'll help you to keep the rhythm steady, creating a rock feel.

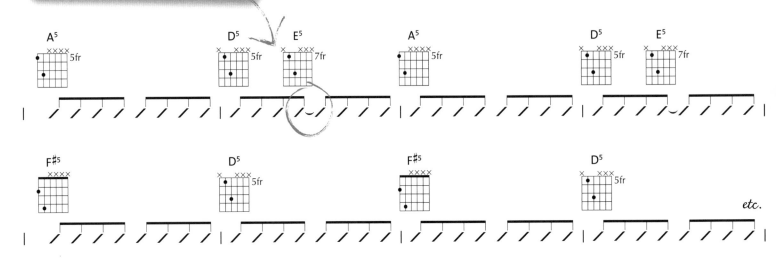

Now, after ten bars, various barre chords are played, lasting a bar each, like so:

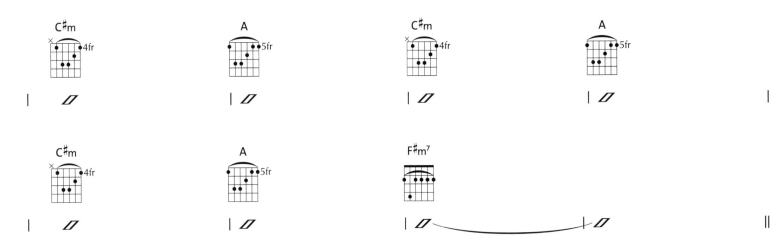

In the second chorus, the barre chord sequence is extended with a further eight bars of alternating C#m and A before the F#m⁷ chord—which itself is repeated.

In chorus 3, the C#m and A section is extended for six bars, before two bars of held F#m⁷ (see the coda section in the song tab).

We now reach the outro section, where the original four-chord riff from the intro returns. Now it's played repeatedly to a fade-out.

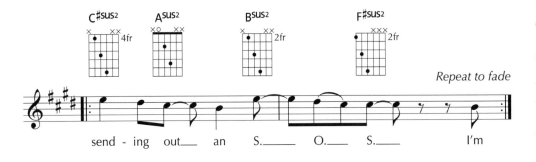

Repeat to fade

send - ing out__ an S.___ O.___ S.___   I'm

53

The Boys Are Back In Town

The twin guitars of Scott Gorham and Brian Robertson create a thick wall of sound in this 1976 classic from Thin Lizzy's Jailbreak album—but there's plenty that a single guitar can do, too!

Intro Chords

The song opens with an intro section that features three power chords—simple two-note shapes played in various places on the fretboard.

The timing of these chords is important: they're all *pushed* forward by an eighth-note, so they're played with up-strums. The A^5 lasts for two bars, with the B^5 and D^5 taking one bar each.

To stop each chord at just the right time, use *palm muting* (opposite).

> ### Palm Muting
>
> Rest the heel of the palm at or very near the bridge and just touching the strings. This will shorten the sustain of the strings, creating a muted effect. This way, the individual notes can be heard very clearly as they don't blend together.

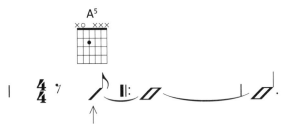

Alternatively, play a single-note line in the second bar. Here's the full tab, with fuller shapes for the power chords, too, as played in the second guitar part.

Again, *push* the chords with up-strums. You'll find a demonstration of this accented up-strum technique at 02:41 in the video.

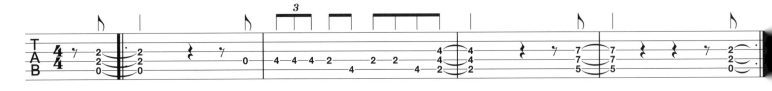

Verse Strumming

For the verse, the rhythm guitar part continues in a similar style, but with a short, accented strum at the end of every held chord.

As before, watch out for the direction of the strumming to help you with the timing, and keep the short strums crisp by using palm muting (see above) right after they're played.

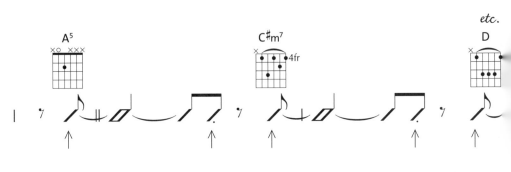

Chorus Riff

03:13

The chorus likewise uses pushed, sustained chords behind the vocals, in a rhythm figure that's identical to the intro. After 12 bars, however, the famous guitar riff is played.

Two parts are given in the tab but, for a single guitar part, play the upper one. Notice the hammer-ons—they'll help you to play in time, especially if you sort out logical fingerings for the phrase.

Reading Triplets

Notice the two different kinds of triplets in this phrase. Firstly, triplet eighth-notes (all played within a single quarter-beat); then at the end of the phrase, triplet quarter-notes (played to fit into two standard quarter-beats).

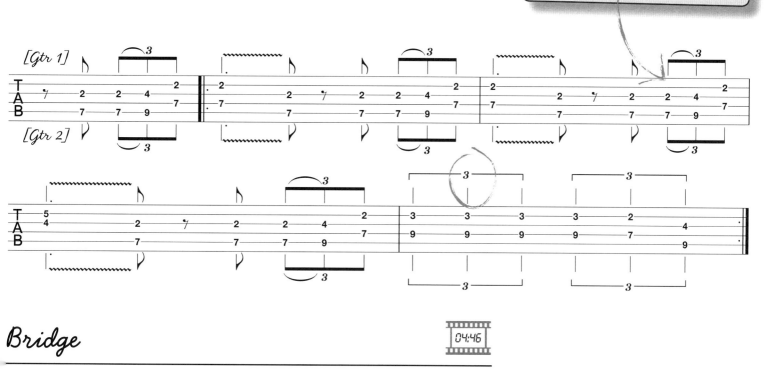

Bridge

04:46

The bridge comes after two verses and choruses. It's a 16-bar section that features Dsus^4 and D strummed in triplet eighths.

This is followed by the familiar pushed rhythms on various chords including more sus^4 shapes. Here's the whole thing:

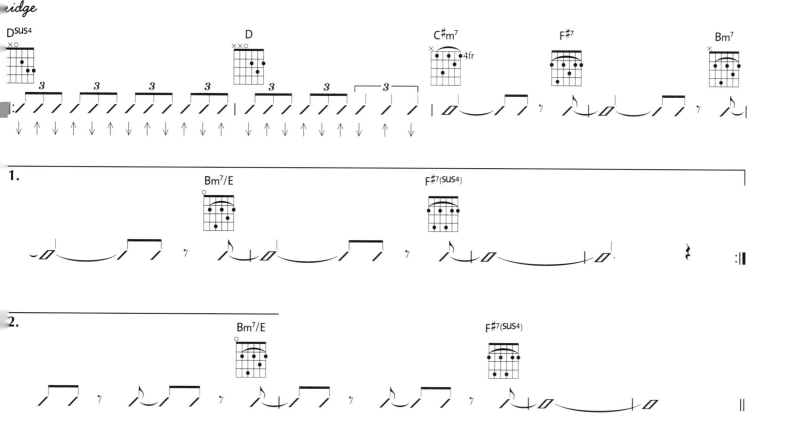

Finally, there's an extended outro section. After the final chorus, we have a new eight-bar passage played twice.

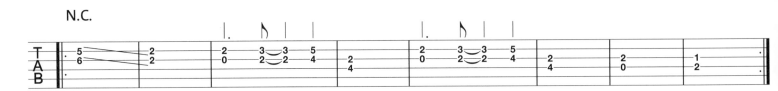

After the second play-through of this passage, the familiar chorus riff enters again. This continues to the end of the song.

Once it's played twice, a third guitar part, harmonising the other two, comes in:

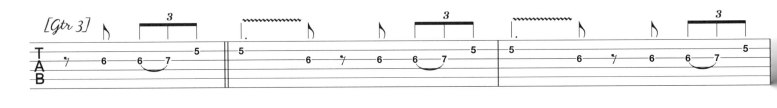

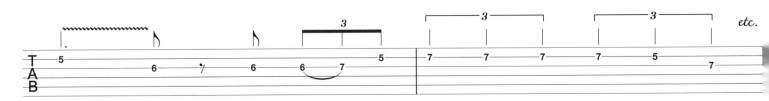

And, four bars later, a fourth guitar part can also be added:

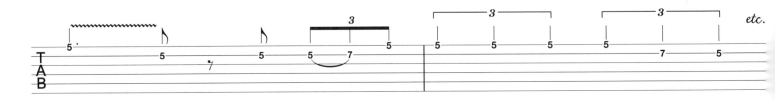

The song ends with these four-bar phrases repeating to a fade-out.

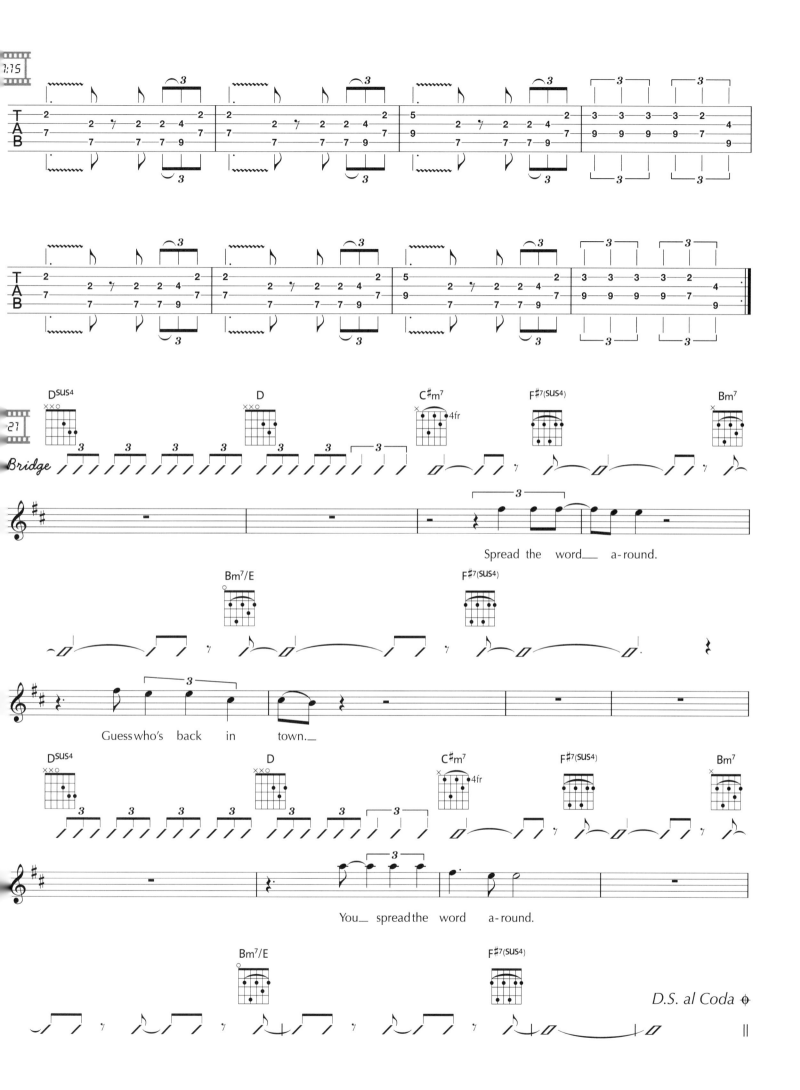

60

The boys_ are back_ in town_

_ a- gain._

Been hang-ing down at

[Add gtr 3]

Di - no's._

[Add gtr 4]

The boys are back_ in town_

Repeat guitars to fade

_ a - gain.__

Reading Tablature

Guitar tablature—or 'tab'—is a system of notation based on a set of six lines, each representing a string of the guitar.

The music is divided into sections of equal length called *bars* or *measures* shown with bar lines.

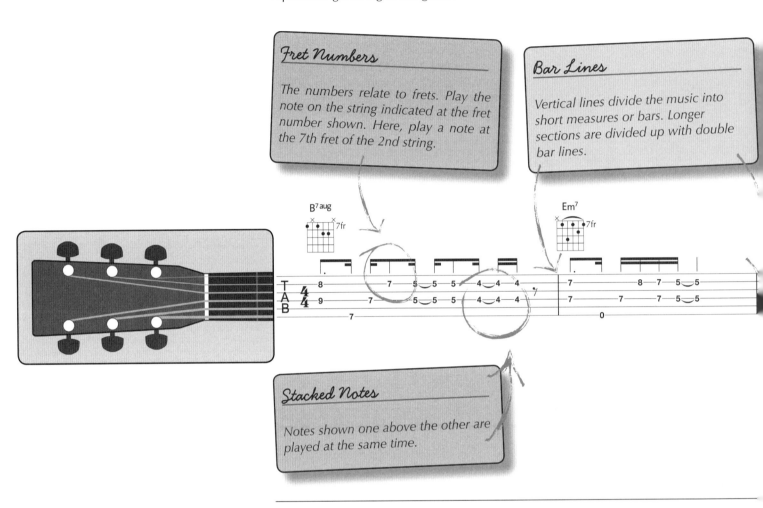

Fret Numbers

The numbers relate to frets. Play the note on the string indicated at the fret number shown. Here, play a note at the 7th fret of the 2nd string.

Bar Lines

Vertical lines divide the music into short measures or bars. Longer sections are divided up with double bar lines.

Stacked Notes

Notes shown one above the other are played at the same time.

The *time signature* at the start of the music will tell you how many beats each bar has.

The top number gives the beat count, while the bottom number indicates what kind of note value is used to show the beat.

In this example (*right*) the music has four beats in the bar, and the note value used for one beat is a quarter-note. Quarter-notes are by far the commonest type of beat and are almost universally used in rock and pop music.

Time Signature Changes

Occasionally, a bar with a different number of beats appears. This is shown by a new, temporary time signature.

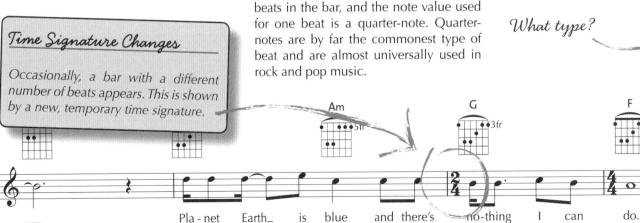

Pla - net   Earth_   is   blue   and there's   no-thing   I   can   do.
Pla - net   Earth_   is   blue   and there's   no-thing   I   can   do.

Reading Rhythms

Apart from the standard music notation used for the vocal line, both the strumming patterns and guitar tab have rhythm tails: a special notation that makes it easy to see how long a note lasts—and when no note is played, too.

Let's look at the way rhythms are shown in strumming patterns.

Firstly, a **whole note**, lasting a bar of 4/4. An absence of notes is called a *rest*. In the UK, whole notes are known as *semibreves*.

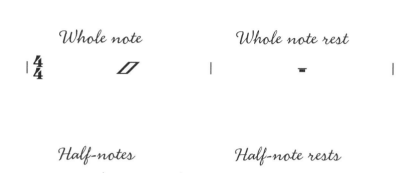

A **half-note**, or *minim*, lasts half as long as a whole note. In 4/4 it's worth two beats. Here's a bar each of half notes and half note rests.

A **quarter-note**, or *crotchet*, is worth a quarter of a whole-note. It represents a single beat in 4/4.

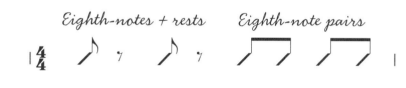

Dividing quarter-notes in half creates **eighth-notes**. These can appear singly—with a hook on the stem; or else in pairs—with a beam joining them. Eighth-note rests are also shown.

The smallest commonly-used rhythm value is the **sixteenth-note**, or *semiquaver*. These appear singly or in groups of up to four together (a single beat).

Adding a dot after any note creates a time value of half as much again. A **dotted quarter**, for instance, is worth three eighths. A **dotted half** is worth three quarters. Notice that dotted eighths are paired with single sixteenths to make a whole beat.

Notes are joined together to create unusual time values or to continue across a bar line. Curved lines called **ties** are used to connect notes into a single note.

You'll find guitar tablature *with* rhythm tails, and other tablature *without* (often used together with standard guitar notation). This book uses tab with rhythm tails, to give you more precise information. The tails follow almost precisely the same rules as for strumming rhythms, with one exception which we'll look at now.

Here's a strumming pattern with the equivalent in guitar tab below. The rhythm tails and rests are exactly the same.

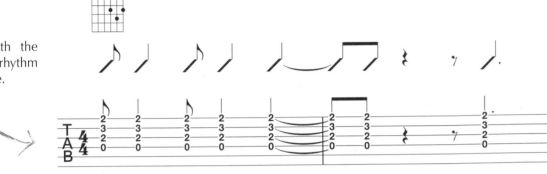

In tablature, half-notes have a rhythm tail which is identical to a quarter-note.

However, it's almost always easy to tell half-notes from quarter-notes by their position in the bar and/or other notes and rests around it.

A whole note, of course, has no tail at all.

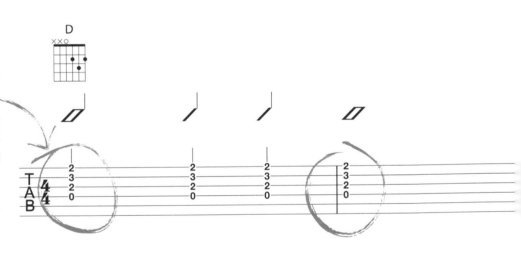

The arrangements in this book include full tablature for the guitar part of every riff, strumming or picking part you'll need.

Where the same part reappears later in the song, it's generally indicated in square brackets (*right*).

So look out for these instructions: they'll refer to a part already played, or else a detail covered in the tutorial section.

[Picking as chorus]

Guitar Instructions

Watch out for these labels in the music. They'll show you what to play for any part that's already previously appeared in tablature.